There Is a

by Liza Charlesworth

ISBN: 978-1-338-78282-0
Illustrated by Michael Robertson
Copyright © 2021 by Liza Charlesworth. All rights reserved.
Published by Scholastic Inc., 557 Broadway, New York, NY 10012

10 9 8 7 6 5 4 3 2 1   68   21 22 23 24 25 26 27/0

Printed in Jiaxing, China. First printing, June 2021.

SCHOLASTIC

Oh, no!
There is a goat.

2

Oh, no!
There is a goat
in my box.

3

Oh, no!
There is a goat
in my socks.

Oh, no!
There is a goat
in my plants.

5

Oh, no!
There is a goat
in my pants.

6

Oh, no!
There is a goat
in my chair.

Oh, no!
There is a goat
in my hair.